What Monkey Made

by Liza Charlesworth

ISBN: 978-1-338-78284-4
Illustrated by Diego Funck
Copyright © 2021 by Liza Charlesworth. All rights reserved.
Published by Scholastic Inc., 557 Broadway, New York, NY 10012

10 9 8 7 6 5 4 3 2 1   68   21 22 23 24 25 26 27/0

Printed in Jiaxing, China. First printing, June 2021.

Look what Monkey made.
It is **an** airplane!

Look what Monkey made.
It is **an** octopus!

Look what Monkey made.
It is **an** ice cream cone!

4

Look what Monkey made.
It is **an** elf!

Look what Monkey made.
It is **an** apple!

Look what Monkey made.
It is **an** elephant!

Look what Monkey made.
It is a mess!